Crash

by

Sera Moore Williams

Acknowledgements

Text © Sera Moore Williams 2009
Publication © Atebol Cyf 2009

Published by Atebol, Fagwyr Buildings, Llandre, Aberystwyth,
Ceredigion SY24 5AQ

For permission to use this adaptation by any means other than those listed above, including
performing it in public, a written application should be made to Educational Resources,
WJEC, 245 Western Avenue, Cardiff CF5 2YX, in the first instance.

www.atebol.com

Designed by Ceri Jones, studio@ceri-talybont.com
Cover Image by Andy Freeman
Printed by Y Lolfa, Tal-y-bont, Ceredigion
Sponsered by the Welsh Assembly Government

The play was originally commissioned by the Arad Goch Theatre Company in 2004.

Original Cast
Elin: Rhiannon Morgan
Wes: Dafydd Rhys Evans
Rhys: Rhys ap Trefor
Musician: Owain Llŷr Edwards

Director
Sera Moore Williams
Designer
Andy Freeman
Floor Manager
Llŷr Jones

ISBN 978-1-907004-17-9

SETTING

The playing area, on which all the scenes are played, should be bare. Only the smallest of changes, of minimal props, costume, and furniture, need be made to suggest location.

The musician becomes the DJ for the disco scene.

CHARACTERS

RHYS: A boy who is almost 16. Conscientious. From a supportive background. Not very thin. He's a good friend to Elin.

ELS (ELIN): A girl who is almost 16. From a supportive background.

WES: A boy from a difficult background. Almost 16.

MUSIC.

THE SOUND OF WIND IN THE DISTANCE.

STEVE'S BEDSIT. WES IS ASLEEP ON THE FLOOR (CRASHED OUT). ELIN SITS IN A CORNER, WHERE SHE HAS BEEN ASLEEP. THEIR CLOTHES ARE STREWN UNTIDILY ON THE FLOOR. ELIN STARES AT WES FOR A WHILE BEFORE SHE WAKES HIM WITH A GENTLE SHAKE. HE WAKES WITH A START, FRIGHTENING ELIN.

HE HAS A BAD HANGOVER.

WES: Crap! Crap! Where am I?

ELS: Wes! Calm down!

            SHE KISSES HIM

WES: Where am I?

ELS: Crashed, didn't you?

WES: (SHOCKED) What?

ELS: Crashed, OK?

WES: Where?

ELS: Here!

WES: (RELIEVED TO UNDERSTAND SHE MEANS HE SLEPT) Oh! Oh! OK.

ELS: Alright?

WES: Yeah. (NURSING HIS HEAD) Ouch! (BEAT) Where is everyone?

ELS: Gone.

WES:	Ouch.
	PAUSE.
ELS:	Quiet.
WES:	Not in my head!
ELS:	Just you and me.
WES:	(DISTRACTED) Yeah.
ELIN:	Nobody hassling us.
	PAUSE.
WES:	When did they go?
ELS:	Late. Went to Ben's.
WES:	(SURPRISED) Ben's?
ELS:	Yeah.
WES:	(CONFUSED) So, where are we?
ELS:	(AMUSED) Wes! Steve's place!
WES:	Oh! (BEAT) Did you stay?
ELS:	Yeah.
WES:	Serious? (CHEERING UP) And?
ELS:	What?
WES:	You and me?
ELS:	I don't think so! Here? (BEAT) Anyway you weren't in a fit state really were you? (BEAT) Don't want it to be like that.

PAUSE.

WES: So what about Mammy and Daddy?

ELS: Said I was staying with Sara.

WES: Liar!

ELS: White lie. Not doing anyone any harm am I?

PAUSE.

WES: Got any money?

ELS: Enough for a Coke.

WES: Two Cokes?

ELS: Maybe.

WES: Come on then.

WES NOTICES THE STATE OF HIS CLOTHES.

ELS: Cool. But somewhere quiet OK? Somewhere where we can look at the sea. Takeaway maybe? Craig yr Wylan?

WES: Oh no! All the way up to the top of the cliff? Do we have to? Again?

ELS: (DREAMILY) There'll be waves today.

WES: So?

ELS: Big waves.

WES: Got enough money for a roll? I'm starving!

ELS: Listen to the wind. Can you hear it?

WES:	(REALISING THAT HE'S WET) Oh no! What happened to my jeans? Damp. (DISTRESSED) Oh crap! Please don't say that I …
ELS:	(LAUGHING) No!
WES:	Well how come…?
ELS:	Saved me.
WES:	What?
ELS:	Last night.
WES:	(CONFUSED) Yeah?
ELS:	From the sea.
WES:	(SHOCKED) No way!
ELS:	Don't you remember?
WES:	(UNSURE) Um…
ELS:	On the way home. You saved me!
WES:	Are you sure?
ELS:	Yeah!
WES:	Cool! (BEAT) Crap! Where's my phone?
ELS:	A big fish swam past and ate it!
WES:	What?
ELS:	In my bag Wes!
WES:	Oh! Right! (FETCHING HIS PHONE) Lifeline!

ELS:	Left it by the fire. (WES LOOKS BLANK) My bag. (BEAT) Don't you remember the fire?
WES:	No. Not really!
ELS:	(SHOCKED) Wes!

WES PUTS THE PHONE IN HIS POCKET AND STARTS PUTTING HIS SHOES ON.

WES:	(ABOUT HIS SHOES) Oh! Uh! Wet!
ELS:	Anyway ... You wouldn't have had to be a hero ...
WES:	(DISTRACTED) Haven't got another pair!
ELS:	If you hadn't pushed me in!
WES:	(SHOCKED) No way!
ELS:	Why did you do that?
WES:	Not sure!
ELS:	Off the rocks!
WES:	Crap! Sorry! Angry, were you?
ELS:	No.
WES:	No? (BEAT) Can you swim?
ELS:	Yeah. But not when I'm drunk I don't think!
WES:	(IMPRESSED) Were you drunk?

ELIN NODS HER HEAD.

(BEAT) I can't.

ELS: (SHOCKED) What? Swim?

WES: Not even when I'm sober, sorry!

ELS: You're mad! You jumped in!

           THEY LAUGH

WES: We're lucky to be alive!

           PAUSE.

           So anyway! Now that you know 'bout the evils of vodka,
           (LEANING TOWARDS HER) what are you going to try next?

           HE KISSES HER. SHE PULLS AWAY.

ELS: (BEAT) (AVOIDING THE QUESTION) I didn't drink much.

           PAUSE.

           Wonder what it feels like.

WES: What?

ELS: Drowning.

WES: Wet.

ELS: Funny! (DREAMILY) Warm water all 'round you.

WES: That's crap.

ELS: (DREAMILY) Quiet. Peaceful.

WES: You make it sound like a bath! You'd freeze to death before you
           drowned 'round here, and it wouldn't be peaceful 'cause your teeth
           would be chattering, really loud!

ELS: I'd like to live under the sea. Would you? A mermaid! That's what I'd like to be.

WES: What?

ELS: Would you?

WES: Half man, half kipper? I don't think so.

ELS: What do you want to be then?

WES: International drug dealer!

ELS: No way! (BEAT) I'd like to see one now, would you?

WES: Drug dealer? Yeah. Too right!

ELS: Shut up! A mermaid. I'm sure they're out there!

WES: Nutter!

        PAUSE.

        How come mermaids don't drown?

ELS: What?

WES: Top bit's the same as us yeah? (REFERRING TO ELIN'S BREASTS) Only they've got bigger … than some of us!

ELS: Hoi!

WES: They must have bigger lungs too!

ELS: The sea's the perfect place for them. They belong there. Fit in. That's why they don't drown.

WES: Deep Els!

11

ELS: Oh shut up Wesley!

WES: What?

         PAUSE.

ELS: I don't belong.

WES: What, here?

ELS: No. Home.

WES: Join the club.

ELS: Never going to please Mam and Dad.

WES: I don't bother trying. Stuff 'em.

ELS: That's easy for you to say!

WES: Why?

ELS: You're lucky.

WES: Me?

ELS: You don't live with your parents do you?

WES: No.

ELS: You've got nobody to let down then have you? You're free.

WES: Free? Me?

ELIN: You can do whatever you want to.

         PAUSE.

WES: (CHANGING TACK) So I was a hero last night then yeah?

ELS: Sort of. (BEAT) So?

WES: (FLIRTING) So. Doesn't a hero get a reward?

ELS: (FLIRTING) Like what?

WES: (MOVING IN ON HER) Um …

ELS: (FLIRTING) A medal?

WES: (FLIRTING) No!

ELS: (FLIRTING) What then? Oh! (TEASING) Oh OK. Come on then.

            SHE TICKLES HIM. This? Yeah?

WES: (MOVING AWAY) No! Get off! Ger off will you!

ELS: Ugh! You're damp!

WES: And you!

ELS: We are SO the same.

WES: What?

ELS: Me and you.

WES: Think so? Cool.

ELS: Us against the world OK?

WES: Yeah, if you want.

ELS: My hero.

WES: Yeah? (BEAT. PLAYFUL) Is it a man?

ELS: (JOINING IN THE GAME) Is it a bird?

BOTH: No! It's Super Wes!

            HE PICKS HER UP AND SPINS AROUND

WES: With Super Powers. Come on then. Fly with me. (SPINNING ELIN) Up up up …

ELS: 'Till everyone else is really small.

WES: (SPINNING) Higher and higher …

            THEY SPIN EVER FASTER.

ELS: Until everyone else starts to disappear.

WES: (SPINNING) Higher and higher, and higher. Out of this dump.

            THEY FALL TO THE FLOOR.

ELS: Ouch! Oh! Ouch!

WES: Sorry.

ELS: Ouch! Someone should stick a health warning on you!

WES: Yeah?

ELS: Ouch.

WES: Sorry Els.

            PAUSE. HE STUDIES HER.

            Mermaids are dangerous too aren't they?

ELS: What?

WES: Fit. Make men crash their boats!

ELS: What?

WES: Boats! On the rocks!

ELS: Oh. Yeah. OK.

WES: You're quite fit!

ELS: (TEASING) Quite?

WES: Yeah! Come here.

         THEY KISS. HE GETS SERIOUS. SHE PULLS AWAY.

ELS: Wes don't!

         HE SULKS.

         But soon OK? Somewhere better.

WES: (ENCOURAGED) Yeah? (BEAT) I can get a car if you want?

ELS: What?

WES: Something well cool. (BEAT) Take you somewhere.

ELS: Oh yeah! Right!

WES: Somewhere better. Would you come?

ELS: You can't drive.

WES: No?

ELS: (SURPRISED) What?

WES: Would you come with me?

ELS: I don't know. Can you drive?

WES: Would you come with me if I could?

ELS: Maybe.

WES: Cool.

ELS: You're cool. (BEAT) I love you.

WES: Yeah?

ELS: And?

          PAUSE. WES DOES NOT RESPOND.

          (CERTAIN) You love me too.

WES: Do I?

ELS: Yes! I know you do.

WES: Yeah?

ELS: Yes. Girls know these things Wes. I'm telling you.

MUSIC.
THE SOUND OF THE SCHOOL CANTEEN. RHYS AND
ELIN ARE EATING ROLLS.

RHYS: How do you know?

ELS: Just do OK. (REFERRING TO HER ROLL) Want this?

RHYS: (ENTHUSIASTIC) Yeah!

          RHYS STUFFS BOTH ROLLS INTO HIS MOUTH.

ELS: Rhys!

RHYS: (BEAT) Bet he's had loads of girls.

ELS: No he hasn't. And anyway, this is different. Right?

          PAUSE.

          Why were you late this morning?

RHYS: Tractor.

ELS: What?

RHYS: On the wibbly wobbly way.

ELS: What?

RHYS: That's what Jen calls the road from our place.

ELS: Oh. (BEAT) Wish I had a sister.

RHYS: What for?! (BEAT) No room to pass is there.

ELS: On the wibbly wobbly way?

RHYS: Yeah. Dad's racing track, Mam calls it.

ELS: (SMILING) Yeah?

            RHYS MAKES RACING CAR SOUNDS.

RHYS: Yeah. Have you seen my Dad driving? Brilliant. O-60 in a
            nanosecond!

ELS: A what?

RHYS: G-force hits his face (GRIMACING) like that! (AS RACING
            COMMENTATOR) 'And he's on two wheels on the first bend!'

ELS: Sounds dangerous.

RHYS: No! There's no one else on our road is there usually? But 20 miles an
            hour all the way this morning, behind the Fergie! Dad gave the
            driver loads of abuse!

ELS: Did he?

RHYS: Yeah. Farmer next door. Dad didn't care. (IMPRESSED) Road rage!
            It's a wonderful thing!

            PAUSE.

            So what's he got that I haven't got eh?

ELS: Who? Your Dad?

RHYS: Oh ugh Elin! Gross. No! Wesley.

ELS: Sexy body?

RHYS: Cow!

ELS: Sorry.

RHYS: You will be! When I'm a lawyer and he's on benefits!

ELS: Shut up. Wes won't be on benefits, right?

RHYS: Yeah?

ELS: He's just as clever as you are.

RHYS: No money! How sexy is that?

ELS: Oh shut up.

RHYS: Or he might be in jail!

ELS: He won't be! You don't know anything about him! He's had a hard time.

RHYS: Yeah. So?

ELS: Gets moved around all the time.

RHYS: So?

ELS: I'm happy with him.

RHYS: (UNDULATING HIS STOMACH. LIKE A BELLY DANCER, MUCH TO ELIN'S SURPRISE) Yeah?

ELS: (WATCHING RHYS) We understand each other.

RHYS: How come? (BEAT. ABOUT HIS STOMACH.) I've got a flat-pack.

ELS: (CONFUSED) What?

RHYS: Want to see it?

         HE LIFTS HIS SHIRT!

ELS: Six pack Rhys!

RHYS: I know! (ABOUT HIS BELLY) I can ripple it!

RHYS DOES HIS VERSION OF A BELLY DANCE.

ELS: (IN DISGUST) Oh! Put it away. Don't be disgusting!

RHYS: Fair enough Chocolate Chip!

ELS: (BEAT) I can chill when I'm with him. He knows how things get with parents.

RHYS: Yeah? (BEAT) Has he been to your place?

ELS: No. He doesn't want to.

RHYS: Oh.

RHYS DOES A YOGA POSITION.

ELS: (WATCHING IN AMAZEMENT) Why would he?

RHYS: Yeah.

ELS: Rhys! What are you doing?

RHYS: Yoga!

ELS: Whatever! Anyway, my parents would stop me seeing him if he came 'round.

RHYS: 'Cause he's a psycho?

ELS: No!

RHYS: Freak?

ELS: No! Shut up! He's not. OK? (BEAT) They don't want me to have a life. That's why.

RHYS: 'Life starts after exams', Elin!

ELS: If they could fast-forward me about five years, they would.

RHYS: Pubes, acne, and parents who lose the plot. It's great being our age!

ELS: The only thing that matters to my parents is what I'm going to do!

RHYS: Well, what are you going to do?

ELS: Rhys! Shut up! You're like an old woman!

RHYS: Sexist.

ELS: Shut up will you. I don't know yet do I?

RHYS: They're all the same Els.

ELS: No way! My parents are the worst.

RHYS: They're all the same I'm telling you! Forty somethings. Programmed to be a pain! Clones!

ELS: You're OK with it all though aren't you?

RHYS: Yeah, suppose.

ELS: You're lucky. Never ever going to do anything wrong are you?

RHYS: Probably not!

ELS: Never going to disappoint anyone.

RHYS: Els, what's wrong?

          PAUSE.

ELS: I'm leaving at the end of this year.

RHYS: (SHOCKED) What? No way!

ELS: I've had enough.

RHYS: Leaving school? Since when? No way! No way!

MUSIC.

THE SOUND OF A SCHOOL YARD. WES AND ELS ARE
TALKING. RHYS IS ON HIS OWN, EATING CRISPS.

ELS: No way Wes OK.

WES: Not good enough am I?

ELS: You are!

WES: Too different aren't we?

ELS: We're not! (SEEING RHYS) Hi!

WES: (TO RHYS. ANGRY) Get lost!

            RHYS EXITS IN A HURRY.

            (TO ELS) Wouldn't fit in would I?

ELS: Yes you would!

WES: Well let me come 'round then.

ELS: What for?

WES: Meet the in-laws!

ELS: No way! Why?

WES: Just want to.

ELIN: Why?

            WES SHRUGS.

            I've got to work tonight. Got to revise, or they'll go off on one
            again.

WES: Yeah?

ELIN: Yes.

WES: There's a month or something until your exams.

ELS: Whose exams?

WES: I'm not doing them.

ELS: What?

WES: What for? Nobody'll care.

ELS: You're lucky. That's so not fair.

         PAUSE.

         I've fallen out with them already today. They'd go psych if anyone
         came home with me.

WES: Oh.

ELS: And you don't want to see my Dad in a temper, believe me!

WES: No? (BEAT) I ended up in casualty once when my Dad lost it.

ELS: (SHOCKED) Yeah? (BEAT) Bullies, all of them, aren't they?

WES: It wouldn't happen now I'm telling you! (ANGRY) And if your Dad
         touches you …

ELS: What?

WES: If your Dad starts on you again OK, just say.

         ALTHOUGH ELIN'S DAD DOESN'T BEAT HER, SHE
         DOESN'T CORRECT WES'S MISTAKE.

24

ELS: (BEAT) Yeah. (BEAT) OK.

WES: I'll sort him out for you.

ELS: Yeah. (BEAT) Cool.

         PAUSE.

         Things'll be different soon. Promise. We'll be able to spend more time together and things, after exams.

WES: Yeah? (BEAT) I've never been out with anyone that long.

ELS: (CONCERNED) No?

WES: (NOTICING HER CONCERN) No.

ELS: (DEFLATED) Oh.

         PAUSE.

WES: (TAKING ADVANTAGE OF HER INSECURITY) Got any time today? After school? Before you go home?

ELS: What for?

WES: (PLEADING) Go 'round to Ben's?

ELS: Ben's?

WES: Yeah. His place is OK isn't it?

ELS: (UNSURE) Well ... um ...

WES: Better than Steve's place!

ELS: (HESITANT) Um, well, will there be anyone in?

WES: Yeah. But he'll go out if I ask him.

ELS: Yeah?

WES: Yeah. If we want him to.

ELS: (HESITANT) Oh.

WES: We've got nowhere else have we?

ELS: (BEAT) Well! … (STILL UNSURE) OK.

WES: We are serious yeah?

ELS: Are we?

WES: Well I am. Are you?

ELS: Yes. (BEAT) (WITH MORE CONVICTION) OK then.

WES: Yeah? (DELIGHTED) Sure?

ELS: Um…

WES: Cool! (SCHOOL BELL RINGS) What have you got this afternoon?

ELS: Maths first. What have you got?

WES: Going to town. But Ben's place OK? Half past three.

ELS: (HESITANT) Um … Don't know. Perhaps!

WES: Oh come on Els! Please. (WES KISSES HER) I love you.

ELS: (PLEASED) What? What did you say?

WES: Nothing.

ELS: Yes you did!

WES: No!

ELS: Heard you Wes. (BEAT) I love you too. But you said it first this
            time! (ELIN KISSES HIM QUICKLY) I'm going OK? See you.

WES: Ben's place?

ELS: (CERTAIN) Yes.

WES: Definite?

ELS: Yes.

            ELS EXITS. WES IS VICTORIOUS.

WES: Yes!

MUSIC.

A NOISY CLASSROOM.

RHYS IS EATING CRISPS DISTRACTEDLY. ELIN ENTERS, TIRED. SHE RESTS HER HEAD ON RHYS' KNEE, ACCIDENTLY CRUSHING HIS CRISPS.

ELS: (GLAD OF THE OPPORTUNITY TO REST) Yes!

RHYS: (PANIC STRICKEN) No! (ABOUT THE CRISPS) You've got hair in my bag!

ELS: Rhys! Don't shout!

RHYS: Where were you last night? Major disaster!

ELS: Yeah?

RHYS: Ten o'clock right, and I lost everything!

ELS: (ONLY HALF LISTENING) I doubt it!

RHYS: I did! (REALISING THAT ELIN IS TIRED) Els, what's the matter? Are you OK?

ELS: I'm shattered Rhys.

RHYS: Yeah?

ELS: Yeah. So shut it.

RHYS: Why?

ELS: 'Cause you're giving me a headache.

RHYS: No! Why are you shattered?

ELS: Sleep-over Rhys! With Sara.

RHYS: You're never home.

ELS: I wish!

RHYS: Always out.

ELS: So? (BEAT) Rhys (ABOUT THE CRISPS) why are you stuffing those?

RHYS: Stressed Els.

ELS: What flavour?

RHYS: Eating disorder.

ELS: What?

RHYS: Salt and vinegar!

ELS: Oh! Puke!

RHYS: Comfort eating Els, 'cause I'll have to do it all again now.

ELS: (CONFUSED) What?

RHYS: Geog.

ELS: What?

RHYS: Homework.

ELS: (REMEMBERING) Oh no!

RHYS: And if my computer crashes again … I'm going to throw it out of my window.

ELS: On to your Dad's new car?

RHYS: Yes! (BEAT) Well no, maybe not!

ELS: Why's your Dad got a car like that?

RHYS: What! A TVR, four litre, six cylinder …

ELS: Whatever! Is he on the pull, or what?

RHYS: Elin! That's my dad you're on about! He's got to travel all the time
          hasn't he with his job? Needs a good car. (BEAT) I'm going to have
          a Subaru Impreza or a (HE LISTS A RANGE OF SPORTY
          CARS) when I start driving. (BEAT) Was it Sara's birthday?

ELS: What? (UNDERSTANDING) No.

RHYS: Girly night in? Yeah?

ELS: Leave it OK?

RHYS: Brain masks and nose spas and things?

ELS: Rhys!

RHYS: Watching chick-flicks 'till who knows when! What was it? *Miss
          Congeniality?* Yeah? (SINGING AS IN FILM) He wants to love
          you. He wants to marry you! (SPEAKING) Oh! Were you all
          wearing pyjamas? Oh! I'd have loved to have been there!

ELS: Rhys! I'm shattered, OK?

RHYS: OK. (BEAT) Els.

ELS: What?

RHYS: Can I borrow yours?

ELS: What?

RHYS: The homework. Please? Only this time. I'll do whatever you want.
          I'll be your slave. (BEAT) Oh no! (DEFLATED) You haven't done
          it have you?

ELS: Correct!

RHYS: O no!

ELS: Rhys!

RHYS: Biatch! I'm doomed.

ELS: Just leave me alone will you?

RHYS: I wanted to borrow it!

ELS: Oh, sorry!

RHYS: Oh well, at least both of us'll get a bollocking now. Not just me.

ELS: I don't care.

RHYS: Well I do. A bit! Think Mr Jones will believe me?

ELS: (TEASING) No.

RHYS: (ADAMANT) But I'm telling the honest-to-God truth!

ELS: Yeah, right!

RHYS: (UPSET) It crashed.

ELS: Rhys.

RHYS: I'm telling you! The computer crashed.

ELS: I know.

RHYS: (UPSET) Piece of ...

ELS: Rhys!

RHYS: What?

ELS: Just shut up, OK? I don't care what crashed. Just log off will you.

RHYS: What?

ELS: Log off!

RHYS: What?

ELS: Now!

THE SOUND OF TRAFFIC. WES IS ON THE SIDE OF A
BUSY ROAD, TALKING TO HIS SOCIAL WORKER ON HIS
MOBILE.

WES: Where? (BEAT. LISTENING) No way! I'm alright where I am
        aren't I? (BEAT. LISTENING) Why can't I? (BEAT. LISTENING)
        They're having you on Mike (BEAT. LISTENING), I do sleep
        there.

        (BEAT. LISTENING)

        Yeah OK, OK sometimes I don't. (BEAT. LISTENING) Well why
        can't I go back to where I was before them then? (BEAT.
        LISTENING) Yeah. They were OK. (BEAT. LISTENING) Oh.
        (BEAT. LISTENING) No way man. No way. Why can't I go back
        to my old man's house then? (BEAT. LISTENING) I know he is.
        (BEAT. LISTENING) I know he doesn't (BEAT. LISTENING) I
        don't care. I could handle it now. (BEAT. LISTENING) I could. I
        know what they're like. (BEAT. LISTENING) Why can't I? (BEAT.
        LISTENING) No! You tell me. You're the social worker! (BEAT.
        LISTENING) OK. OK! (BEAT. LISTENING) Yes! I'll say sorry,
        but it's not fair. (BEAT. LISTENING) Yes! Tonight! I'll go (BEAT.
        LISTENING) OK. Tonight. (BEAT) Yes!

MUSIC.

BEN'S PLACE.

THE ATMOSPHERE IS SUBDUED. A BAD-TEMPERED
WES IS SWIGGING FROM A VODKA BOTTLE WHILST
TEXTING. ELIN LOOKS ON SULKILY.

ELS: (RE TEXT) Who's that?

WES: Steve.

ELS: Why are you texting him? (BEAT) Wes, I want to talk to you.

WES: Yeah? (BEAT) I don't want to, OK? (BEAT) You're too serious
         sometimes, that's all I said.

ELS: You're supposed to be serious about me too!

WES: I am.

ELS: Well ask Ben then. (BEAT) Please? (BEAT) Ben'll let us stay here, if
         you ask him, maybe.

WES: He won't! (BEAT) And I've got to crash where I'm meant to
         sometimes OK?

ELS: I don't want to go home.

WES: I get grief off my social worker if I don't turn up. And you don't
         want to live here do you?

ELS: It's better than my place.

WES: No it's not Els.

ELS: It is.

WES: Your place is massive. I've seen it.

ELS: What?

WES: Called 'round, OK? Don't worry. There was no-one in.

ELS: Stalker! (BEAT) Yeah, big house, so what?

WES: So what?

ELS: They pick on me all the time at home.

WES: I know.

ELS: Mental cruelty!

WES: Yes! I know Els.

ELS: They think they own me. Think they've got a right to decide everything for me. They're on my back all the time. (BEAT) Please can I stay here with you Wes? Please?

WES: Why's everything about you all the time?

ELS: What?

WES: Nothing.

ELS: No! What did you say?

WES: Nothing! (BEAT) I'll ask Ben, OK?

ELS: Yeah? Will you?

WES: Yeah. PAUSE. I know how you feel Els.

ELS: You're the only one who gets what it's like.

WES: Parents from hell.

PAUSE. WES OFFERS ELIN SOME VODKA.

Want some?

ELS: Yeah. OK.

SHE DRINKS, AND SPLUTTERS.

WES: Still don't like it do you?

ELS: No. But I like forgetting about all the hassle.

WES: Yeah. Got any money?

ELS: Control freaks.

WES: Els?

ELS: (DRINKING MORE VODKA) Thought police.

WES: Els!

ELS: They'll be sorry.

WES: Have you got any cash?

ELS: Yeah. Eight quid. Dinner money. Why?

WES: At least they remember to feed you!

ELS: God! My mother would come to school and feed me herself with a spoon if they'd let her!

WES: I've got a bit of cash too, so ...

ELS: (DRINKING MORE VODKA) Make sure I'm eating properly. No chips, no crisps, and whatever happens, absolutely nothing fizzy!

WES: (HE SNATCHES THE BOTTLE AWAY FROM HER) Yeah! Well! Lucky vodka's not fizzy then isn't it!

ELS: Yeah. (BEAT) Sad! I don't want to be like my Mam when I grow up.

WES: I don't want to be like my Dad! (BEAT) You don't want school dinners this week do you?

ELS: (CONFUSED) No?

WES: No. It's bad for you! (BEAT) And you've got a day off today.

ELS: Have I? Cool! What for?

WES: (HESITANT) I know where we can buy something.

ELS: Oh. (UNCERTAIN) Yeah? Do you? (BEAT) Oh I'm not sure Wes.

WES: Nothing heavy. Want to?

ELS: (HESITANT) Well, OK then. But only if you promise to look after me.

WES: Hey! Super Wes will do his best! OK. Mission. I'll phone the boys. Can you drive?

ELS: Drive? No!

WES: No? Oh! Want to learn then?

THE MUSICIAN PLAYS 'I BELIVE IN A THING CALLED LOVE', BY THE DARKNESS.
RHYS' BEDROOM. HE'S SINGING ALONG TO THE DARKNESS, PLAYING AIR GUITAR. STOPS TO LISTEN TO HIS MOTHER WHO HAS OBVIOUSLY CALLED OUT TO HIM FROM DOWNSTAIRS TELLING HIM TO TURN HIS MUSIC DOWN.

RHYS: (BAD TEMPERED. ANSWERING) OK Mam. Sorry! (BEAT. LISTENING. ANSWERING) Darkness. (BEAT. LISTENING. ANSWERING) Don't you? I do! (BEAT. LISTENING) OK, OK. Sorry!

HE TURNS THE MUSIC DOWN. HE GOES TO HIS LAPTOP.

(TYPING)

Chocolatechip@hotmail.co.uk.

(BEAT)

Attachment Els. Work from last week. Where were you? Yeah I know. I'm sad.

PAUSE.

(TYPING)

One of The Darkness is bulimic. Confessed in *Hello*. My sister's copy! Obviously! Wanted people to know that eating too much and puking is a boy thing too. I think I'm bulimic, just that I don't do the puking bit. Ho ho, ho ho!

(TO HIMSELF)

So?

(TYPING)

Are you with your druggy no good fat ugly freak brain arse pain –
God, I hate him – boyfriend tonight?

(TO HIMSELF)

Delete! If you want to keep your balls Rhys. They might come in
useful one day, you never know!

(TYPING)

If you're not with Wes tonight, get in touch. No credit on my phone
though. Rhys-love-god-Evans.

(TO HIMSELF)

No. Delete. Definitely delete. (TYPING) Just Rhys.
(TO HIMSELF) Send.
(HE TAKES A LONELY LOOK AT HIS ROOM.
HE SHOUTS DOWNSTAIRS TO HIS MOTHER.) Mam? Can
I have a hot chocolate? (BEAT. LISTENING. TO HIS MOTHER)
Oh, go on! (BEAT. LISTENING) Mean!

MUSIC.

THE SOUND OF THE SCHOOL CANTEEN.

RHYS IS DRINKING FROM A CAN.

RHYS: No! Oh my God!

ELS: I'm shattered.

RHYS: You're mad!

ELS: You're the only one who knows. So don't tell.

RHYS: OK.

ELS: Mam and Dad would go ballistic.

RHYS: Don't they notice you're not there?

ELS: Yeah. Sometimes. They think I'm with people they know though.

RHYS: Sara?

ELS: Yeah. And you!

RHYS: Me? Oh cheers! (BEAT) You're nuts.

ELS: It's a buzz Rhys!

RHYS: Better than snogging me in year 6?

ELS: That was a bet! 'Snog-a-Gog'!

RHYS: Serious?

ELS: No! Stupid!

RHYS: Elin!

ELS: We've done it loads of times. Middle of town's like a racing track late at night.

RHYS: (AMAZED) Middle of town?

ELS: Yeah!

RHYS: No way! (BEAT) My Dad's going to take me to the beach when I start driving!

ELS: (PATRONISING) Yeah? Great! (BEAT) Rhys. Got any money?

RHYS: No.

ELS: Can't find my bag.

RHYS: Yeah, right.

ELS: What?

RHYS: You've never got any money any more.

ELS: Yeah, well it's not my fault that Mam and Dad forget.

RHYS: Thought you said you'd lost your bag!

ELS: Oh whatever!

PAUSE. RHYS OFFERS ELIN HIS CAN OF COKE.

RHYS: Want some?

ELS: Sure?

RHYS: Yeah.

ELIN DRINKS TOO MUCH.

Hoi! That's my Diet Coke! (BEAT) Don't do it again Els.

ELS: What? Have I got lipstick on your can?

RHYS: No! You know what I mean.

ELS: (RE DRIVING) I like it Rhys! It empties your head.

RHYS: Yeah, but don't Els, please.

ELS: Why? Your Dad drives fast. Why is it OK for him, but not for me?

RHYS: He's got a license!

ELS: Mam and Dad and my stupid exams all disappear. You get rid of all that crap spinning. Everything's a blur. A rush. Everything goes whizzing past.

RHYS: Can't wait till I've got my license!

ELS: Really fast. You feel free, Rhys. You feel alive, OK?

RHYS: Yeah, but it's dangerous.

ELS: Yeah?

RHYS: Yeah. You could die!

ELS: So?

RHYS: Idiot.

ELS: What? (BEAT. ANGRY) Oh I know now why your dad drives fast. Maybe he hopes he's going to hit that tractor on your road one day, head on, so that he never has to listen to you whining on again.

RHYS: (HURT) Get lost Els. (BEAT) Els are you OK?

ELS: I'm fantastic! (BEAT) Wes drove me back, right up to the front gate last night. Seventy over the speed bumps.

RHYS: Yeah. (BEAT) Did your head hit the roof? 'Cause that could explain a lot!

ELS: Hah hah Rhys!

         PAUSE.

RHYS: What sort of car was it?

ELS: Last night? Red.

RHYS: Whose car then?

ELS: How am I supposed to know?

RHYS: What? (BEAT) He's not old enough to drive Els.

ELS: He can, so he does.

RHYS: Yeah, but he's not supposed to, is he!

ELS: (MIMICKING RHYS) 'Not supposed to, is he?' Get a life.

RHYS: Got a life!

ELS: Yeah? You've got no guts, I know that! You'd never do the things me and Wes do.

RHYS: So?

ELS: Playing computer games in your bedroom! Dead cool Rhys!

RHYS: More cool than stealing cars!

ELS: Borrowing, not stealing! You're dead boring.

RHYS: I'm not!

ELS: Mammy and Daddy decide everything for you.

RHYS: They don't. Well OK, they do, but another couple of years, and I'll be on a gap year.

ELS: Gap year? Prat! That's why I'm with him and not with you!

RHYS: What? (BEAT) Would you be with me if it wasn't for him?

ELS: Yeah, right! Don't know if I even like you any more.

           RHYS IS OBVIOUSLY HURT. BEAT.

           We've had enough, Wes and me. We don't give a damn about parents.

RHYS: He doesn't live with his parents though does he?

ELS: He doesn't want to.

RHYS: No?

ELS: No. They were nasty to him, and I know how that feels.

RHYS: (WITH CONTEMPT) No you don't! Your Mam and Dad care about you.

ELS: Oh yeah! Care that I don't misbehave. Care that people don't talk about me.

RHYS: No.

ELS: Care that I pass as many exams as other people's children do.

RHYS: Yeah, well, you're not going to now are you?

ELS: What? (BEAT) Get lost Rhys. You don't know anything, OK? Mam and Dad (HESITATING) … are a pain.

RHYS: Normal life not cool enough for you or what?

ELS: Shut up.

RHYS: You and Wes won't last.

ELS: No?

RHYS: No way.

ELS: I fit in with Wes and his mates.

RHYS: Yeah. Right! Pretend to.

ELS: Pretend?

RHYS: Put on.

ELS: No! (BEAT) I don't fit in at home.

RHYS: No-one our age fits in at home Elin.

ELS: Get lost, OK? Loser.

RHYS: Me?

ELS: Yeah!

RHYS: Me?

ELS: Yeah!

RHYS: Right back at yah!

ELS: Get lost will you.

RHYS: OK, fine!

ELS: Get lost!

RHYS: (BEAT) What, now?

ELS: Yeah!

RHYS: OK. (AS HE EXITS) Going. See?

ELS: Don't want to see you again. Don't know why I bother talking to you. You're just jealous of Wes and me, 'cause nobody would ever fancy you. Geek!

         RHYS EXITS.

         PAUSE. (REGRETTING THE QUARREL) Oh no.

MUSIC.

WES AND ELIN ARE IN A CAFÉ. SHE SEEMS UPSET. HE'S OBVIOUSLY WAITING FOR SOMEBODY.

WES: Where are they?

ELS: Why d'you have to see them again today?

WES: 'Cause I do!

ELS: Why?

WES: 'Cause we're family.

ELS: What?!

WES: Me and the boys. Like family.

ELS: You've got a family Wes.

WES: My parents? Oh yeah! Right!

ELS: No! Not them. Me.

WES: Oh. Yeah. OK. (BEAT) Sorry. (BEAT) Oh, I'm starving. Got any money?

ELS: Use your own.

          PAUSE.

WES: What's wrong? (BEAT) Say.

          ELS SHRUGS.

ELS: Nothing. Sorry. Nothing really.

WES: Something's wrong.

ELS:	Alright then! Everything. OK?
WES:	Me?
ELS:	No. Not you.

PAUSE. ELIN TAKES AN ANGEL PIN OUT OF HER HAND BAG.

Bought this today.

WES:	(DISTRACTED) Cool.
ELS:	Little angel. Quid.
WES:	A quid?
ELS:	Yeah. Want one?
WES:	No.
ELS:	I'll get you one.
WES:	Els! It's a chick thing, OK?
ELS:	If you wear it, it looks after you.
WES:	Like a bodyguard?
ELS:	Sort of.
WES:	You don't need a bodyguard though do you? I'm here to sort things out for you.

PAUSE.

(RE PIN) Did they have a devil, with horns and a tail?

ELS:	No! A devil wouldn't protect you would it?

WES: I don't need protecting. I can look after myself.

ELS: I know.

WES: Got to.

         PAUSE.

         Worried about exams?

ELS: No. (BEAT) Too late now anyway.

WES: Yeah?

ELS: Yeah. Oh I don't know, right? Maybe. I don't care.

         PAUSE.

         Sometimes I do my best to see an angel.

WES: No way!

ELS: Have you ever done that? In bed. 'Please, please please, if you're for real, appear! Now! Come on! Please?' And then, I get scared and go, 'No! Sorry angels, I wasn't serious! Don't come! Please. I really don't want to see you!'

WES: Well don't ask one to visit when I'm there with you.

ELS: Why? Would you be scared?

WES: No! (TEASING) It's just that Ben's bed is crowded enough with only you and me there!

ELS: Shut up! Is that all you think about?

WES: No! (BEAT) I think about football sometimes too!

PAUSE.

ELS: Do you think they exist – angels?

WES: No!

ELS: You're sure?

WES: Yeah.

ELS: Quiet I bet. Think so? Up there.

WES: Up where?

ELS: Beautiful, fluffy, soft.

WES: Earth calling Elin!

ELS: Nobody hassling.

WES: You talk complete crap sometimes!

ELS: No I don't.

WES: What's the matter?

ELS: Everything. I told you!

WES: What?

ELS: An empty feeling.

WES: That's what you get when you don't eat or sleep. It's speed. Next day's crap.

ELS: I'm letting everybody down.

WES: Paranoia! Speed.

ELS: Everybody hates me.

WES: See!

PAUSE.

Has something happened? At home?

ELS: No. (BEAT) Nothing worse than usual.

WES: (THREATENINGLY) I'll sort him out for you. Your dad.

ELS: Yeah. I know. Listen Wes … (BEAT)

ELIN ALMOST ADMITS TO WES THAT SHE'S
MISLEAD HIM ABOUT HER FATHER, BUT CHANGES
HER MIND … You don't have to stay here if you don't want to.

WES: (CONFUSED) What?

PAUSE.

Oh Els! You haven't got something to tell me, have you?

ELS: What? (BEAT. REALISING HE THINKS SHE'S PREGNANT)
No way!

WES: It would be OK. I wouldn't mind. I want loads of kids.

ELS: (SURPRISED) What?

WES: And they're going to get everything.

ELS: Yeah? Now who's talking crap?

WES: What?

ELS: How are they going to have everything, Wes?

WES: I'll sort it.

ELIN: Oh, will you?

WES: Yeah. Big house, like you've got. And loads of fuss. I'm going to love my kids, and they're going to love me. I'm going to work really hard. Seriously.

ELS: Yeah? Starting when? (BEAT) Benefits won't buy a lot.

WES: I'm going to have my own business.

ELS: What? Selling drugs?

WES: No! No way! Hush! (BEAT) Don't know what yet do I?

ELS: Your head's in the clouds.

WES: Me? Well it was you that said it was nice up there!

          PAUSE.

          So you don't want to have my sprogs then?

ELS: I don't know.

WES: You'd be a great mam.

ELS: Wouldn't. Everything's a mess already. (BEAT) I've even fallen out with Rhys.

WES: So?

ELS: We're friends.

WES: Yeah?

ELS: We've been friends for years.

WES: (BEAT) You fancy him don't you?

ELS: I don't.

WES: You do.

ELS: I don't. Right?

WES: (RE RHYS) Posh git.

ELS: Rhys?

WES: You and him are the same aren't you?

ELS: Get lost! I'm not like him, and I don't fancy him. Fallen out with him though, and I'm upset.

WES: (SARCASTIC) Upset! Ooh!

ELS: So upset, it hurts, OK? But I can't expect you to understand that sort of pain can I?

WES: (IN DISBELIEF) What?

ELS: The pain you get when you're worried sick. You haven't got a clue have you?

MUSIC.
THE SOUND OF YOUNG PEOPLE ON THE SCHOOL
YARD. WES IS ATTACKING RHYS. RHYS IS TRYING TO
DEFEND HIMSELF.

RHYS: I can't help it if she's all over me, Wes.

WES: You what?

RHYS: I'm very irresistible.

WES: All over you? All over …

RHYS: Joke mate! Joke. We're friends. That's all.

WES: I don't believe you.

RHYS: No?

WES: No.

RHYS: Crap! (BEAT) OK, OK, I do fancy her.

WES: You what?

RHYS: Yeah yeah, but she doesn't fancy me does she? I mean, look at me!
          Would you fancy that?

WES: (DISGUSTED) You what?

RHYS: Sorry! Sorry! I know you wouldn't. Just trying to… You know to …

WES: Just leave her alone, OK fatso?

RHYS: I've lost three pounds this month!

          PAUSE. WES DOESN'T KNOW WHAT TO SAY.

WES: Is she going to pass her exams?

RHYS:	(SURPRISED) What?
WES:	You heard!
RHYS:	Not as many as she should, maybe.
WES:	And that's my fault is it?
RHYS:	I didn't say that! It's nothing to do with me.
WES:	It's her family's fault.
RHYS:	What?
WES:	They're giving her grief.
RHYS:	They're not! Well, not really.
WES:	They are. Right?
RHYS:	They're not.
WES:	So your parents hassle you 24/7 do they?
RHYS:	Absolutely!

WES DOESN'T BELIEVE HIM.

They do!

WES:	Well (HESITATING) … Does your dad hit you then?
RHYS:	(ASTOUNDED) What?
WES:	You don't know anything then, do you? So shut your mouth, right? I'm going to sort her dad out, if he touches her again.
RHYS:	Sort Mr Jones? No! Don't! No way. He'd never hit Elin. I know him.

WES:	Yeah, right. (HESITANT) Been 'round to her house have you?
RHYS:	Yeah loads of times! (BEAT. WES IS SURPRISED AND HURT) You been?
WES:	Get lost, right.
RHYS:	Right. Sorry! (BEAT) Mr and Mrs Jones are SO not hard! They're vegetarians! They wouldn't hurt Elin. No way.
WES:	Why would Elin lie? She's having a hard time at home, I'm telling you.
RHYS:	Yeah, but, everyone's parents are obsessed with exams.
WES:	Yeah? Well, I wouldn't know would I?
RHYS:	Sorry.
WES:	Get lost.
RHYS:	Thank you.
	RHYS TRIES TO ESCAPE.
WES:	Hoy! Where are you going?
RHYS:	Sorry! I thought you said get lost!
WES:	Prat! (BEAT) Elin wouldn't lie to me.
RHYS:	She would. To fit in.
WES:	With who?
RHYS:	With you!
WES:	What?

RHYS: I know! Strange but true!

WES: (THREATENINGLY) You know everything about everything don't
           you?

RHYS: No! But Elin was fine before she met you!

WES: What?

RHYS: Crap! I can't believe I said that!

WES: What did you say?

RHYS: Sorry, right? Sorry! But Elin's changed. Recently.

WES: So?

RHYS: I'm worried about her.

WES: Get a life.

RHYS: I'll have more of a life than you pal, once I leave home.

WES: Well I'm way ahead of you there, gay-boy!

RHYS: (INSULTED) Excuse me?

WES: I've already left home. Remember?

RHYS: Yeah. But you didn't have any choice did you?

WES: So?

RHYS: Well some of us have got a choice.

WES: Well, lucky you! (BEAT) I've got the sort of parents you can't even
           imagine.

RHYS: Well, sorry, but if I can't imagine them, Elin can't either. Elin's parents love her.

WES: Yeah, right.

          PAUSE.

RHYS: (HESITANT) I think that Elin's bored. I think she's using you.

WES: What?

RHYS: Not on purpose, but ...

WES: She loves me.

RHYS: She thinks she does.

WES: And I love her!

RHYS: (SURPRISED) No way!

WES: What?

RHYS: You don't know what love is.

WES: What?

RHYS: How can you? No offence.

WES: That's not true.

RHYS: Sorry but ...

WES: I know what it is, right? And I know other people get it and I don't. But I'm getting it now, and I like it.

RHYS: That's just sex.

WES: You think it's only that? Jealous are you? (BEAT) She loves me, OK? And I love her. (BEAT. THREATENING) You know what your problem is? Although you go to school every day, like a good little boy, nobody's ever taught you a lesson have they?

RHYS: Yeah, yeah! They have! (RHYS TRIES TO DEFEND HIMSELF BUT TO NO AVAIL) Crap!

WES HITS HIM.

No!

QUIET MUSIC.

ELIN IS BORED IN HER BEDROOM. WES IS UPSET AT
BEN'S PLACE. RHYS IS IN HIS BEDROOM INJURED.

ELIN CALLS WES.

HIS PHONE RINGS BUT SEEING THAT IT'S ELIN
CALLING, HE DOESN'T RESPOND.

ELS: (EXASPERATED) Wes!

SHE TEXTS.

Where are you? Waited for you, yesterday. I'm bored. Want to see you.

SHE SENDS THE TEXT.

OK.

WES RECEIVES THE TEXT.

WES: (READING) Bored? Bitch.

WES THROWS DOWN HIS PHONE. HE CRIES.

ELS: Rhys then.

ELIN TEXTS RHYS.

Sorry 'bout falling out. Miss you babes. Why not in school? Disco Monday. Fancy dress. Xx Els.

ELIN SENDS THE TEXT.

OK.

RHYS RECEIVES THE TEXT, AND REPLIES BY TEXT.

RHYS: Not well. Back Monday. Fancy dress. Yeah baby.

RHYS SENDS HIS TEXT. ELIN RECEIVES IT. SHE SMILES.

LOUD DISCO MUSIC. DISCO LIGHTS FLASH. THE
DJ/MUSICIAN AD-LIBS TO AUDIENCE. SCHOOL DISCO.
ALL ARE DRUNK.

WES, IN HIS USUAL CLOTHES, APPEARS, AND FINDS A
PLACE TO SIT.

ELIN APPEARS, DRESSED AS AN ANGEL. SHE'S ALSO
DRUNK. SHE SEARCHES FOR WES BUT CAN'T FIND HIM.

RHYS APPEARS DRESSED AS A DEVIL. HE'S A BIT
DRUNK. HE DANCES ALONE, UNTIL ELIN FINDS HIM.

ELS: Alright Rhys?

RHYS: Yeah. Are you?

ELS: Yeah.

            WES WATCHES FROM A DISTANCE. RHYS IS AWARE OF
            HIM.

            Dance?

RHYS: (NERVOUS) No! Better not! (BEAT) Mam's in the car park.
            (BEAT) Waiting for me.

ELS: Oh! (REFERRING TO HIS COSTUME) Evil tonight aren't you?
            Dare devil! (BEAT) I'm going now too.

RHYS: Home?

ELS: (LOOKING FOR WES) No.

RHYS: (DISAPPOINTED) Oh. Still with him?

ELS: Leave it.

RHYS: Pleasure! See you tomorrow.

ELS:	Rhys? Have you been drinking?
RHYS:	(COY) Maybe!
ELS:	Well don't breathe on any of the teachers, OK?
RHYS:	Crap! Yeah! OK. OK.

RHYS EXITS. ELIN GRABS WES. HE'S RESISTANT.

ELS:	Wanna go.
WES:	So?
ELS:	Coming?
WES:	No.
ELS:	What's wrong? (BEAT) Oh come on. Please?
WES:	Don't want to.
ELS:	(TEASING) You're being weird again!
WES:	Yeah? (BEAT) I'm not coming.
ELS:	Why?
WES:	Just not.
ELS:	Why?
WES:	Just not. Get lost, and don't say why again.
ELS:	(TEASING) Why?
WES:	I've had enough, OK?
ELS:	Of what?

WES:	Everything.
ELS:	What have I done now?
WES:	Poor little posh girl!
ELS:	(TEASING) Me posh, you Becks!
WES:	Yeah, well, get lost! Always complaining.
ELS:	What?
WES:	I want to stay here.
ELS:	You didn't even want to come here!
WES:	Yeah. With you. I didn't want to come here with you.
ELS:	What? I don't get it!
WES:	Go, will you! If Mr Evans smells that vodka, you'll be in trouble.
ELS:	What? So? I don't care. Please? Just come on.
WES:	(VEHEMENTLY) I don't want to! And I don't want to go out with you any more, right? Get it now, do you? Nobody makes me look a fool.
ELS:	I haven't. What have I done?
WES:	Just get lost!
ELS:	(UPSET) I love you.
WES:	No you don't. Just get lost, and leave me alone.
ELS:	No!

WES: (WES LOSES CONTROL, ALMOST STRIKING ELIN) Get lost, or I'm telling you ....

ELS: (SCARED) What?

WES: Does your dad hit you?

ELS: What?

WES: Does he?

ELS: What? (BEAT) No. (BEAT) But I never said he did.

WES: (UPSET) You let me think so.

ELS: Sorry.

WES: Why? Bored were you?

ELS: (SURPRISED) No! (BEAT) Wanted you to look after me maybe.

WES: You've got plenty of people to do that already. I've got no-one.

ELS: What?

WES: Nothing.

ELS: (BEAT) I'm not happy at home.

WES: Well, try harder then yeah. Maybe that'll help.

ELS: (UPSET) Wes.

WES: Try harder Elin. Just get lost and go home to Mammy and Daddy.

ELS: (UPSET) Wes.

WES: Just get lost, OK?

        ELIN IS LEFT IN TEARS AS WES WALKS AWAY.

MUSIC. THE SOUND OF WIND. A CLIFF TOP.

ELIN IS IN TEARS. STILL DRESSED AS AN ANGEL. SHE PHONES RHYS. SHE BECOMES MORE AND MORE DISTRESSED AS THE SCENE UNFOLDS.

RHYS'S BEDROOM. RHYS IS ASLEEP, STILL WEARING HIS DEVIL'S HORNS. HIS PHONE WAKES HIM. HE'S VERY HUNG-OVER FROM THE DISCO.

RHYS: Bloody hell Elin! What do you want?

ELS: Rhys?

RHYS: What? I'm ill.

           PAUSE.

           I'll get in trouble if Mam wakes up.

ELS: Rhys.

RHYS: I'm ill Els.

ELS: Rhys! Please!

RHYS: Why are you hassling me?

ELS: Please?

RHYS: What? (BEAT) Are you drunk?

ELS: I need help.

RHYS: Yeah, well, I know that!

           PAUSE.

                          Els?

ELS: I don't know what to do.

RHYS: What?

ELS: I don't know what to do.

RHYS: Why?

ELS: Rhys. Please.

RHYS: Bloody hell! Why me?

ELS: Don't know what to do.

RHYS: Yeah. You said!

ELS: I've had enough.

RHYS: Well, what am I supposed to do? Phone the Samaritans.

              LONG PAUSE.
              RHYS REALISES THAT SOMETHING IS SERIOUSLY
              WRONG.

              Crap! Elin? Where are you?

ELS: Craig yr Wylan.

RHYS: (SHOCKED) What? On the cliff? Why?

ELS: Between the clouds and the waves. Big waves down there.

RHYS: What?

ELS: Does the sea ever sleep? I'm tired Rhys.

RHYS:	Crap! Don't go near the edge Els. Els? Els? Where's Wes?
ELS:	We're finished. I want everything to stop going wrong.
RHYS:	Els. (PAUSE) Els. (PAUSE) Elin!
ELS:	Everyone hassling me.
RHYS:	Who?
ELS:	Everyone, OK?
RHYS:	They're not Elin!
ELS:	And I've had enough.
RHYS:	You're drunk. This is silly!
ELS:	Nobody cares about me.
RHYS:	Of course they do, Els.
ELS:	Do you?
RHYS:	Yeah.
ELS:	Well come and get me then.
RHYS:	Who me? Craig yr Wylan? How? I can't.
ELS:	See!
RHYS:	It's two o'clock in the morning Els. Mam's been in bed for hours, and Dad's not back yet.
ELS:	I don't want them to come. I want you!
RHYS:	Me Els? I can't.

ELS: See! There's nobody there when you really need them is there?

RHYS: Elin. Elin. (BEAT) OK. Stay where you are!

ELS: I don't fit in, do I? Can't please anyone, can I? Space, that's all I want. Everything's crashing down all 'round me.

RHYS: OK. Just sit down and wait for me. I'll borrow Mam's car. I'm coming, OK? I'll be there now.

ELS: Rhys.

RHYS: We'll talk, OK? You and me. I'm getting Mam's keys now right?

ELS: Rhys.

RHYS: I'll be there now. Just don't move, OK? I'll be there now.

         UNNOTICED BY ELIN, WES ARRIVES AT THE CLIFF TOP. HE'S INJURED, UPSET, AND CLUTCHING A BOTTLE OF VODKA.

ELS: Had enough, Rhys. Please.

RHYS: OK. OK.

WES: Els?

ELS: (SHOCKED) Wes!

         SHE RUNS TO HIM. HE PUSHES HER AWAY.

WES: Thought this is where you'd be. Had enough have you? Have you?

         ELIN SEES THAT WES IS INJURED.

ELS: What's that?

WES: Life too hard for you is it?

ELS: What's happened?

WES: Crash.

ELS: What?

WES: A crash, OK?

ELS: You're bleeding!

WES: So?

ELS: Were you driving?

WES: Yeah. So?

ELS: Wes!

WES: Fast! Really fast. Down the main drag. Sounds full blast. People on their way home, staring. (SHOUTING) 'Out of the way. Out of the way, OK?' Hand down hard on the horn. Blaring. Cops? Anyone? (SHOUTING) 'Come on. Come on! Where are you? Do something! Anything. Stop me will you?' Handbrake turn. Brakes screeching. Right at the bottom of town. Right there. I stop. (SHOUTING) 'Come on. Nobody. I'm here. Look at me. I'm here. Waiting for you. Race you!' Nobody. Rev the engine. Rubber burning. Nobody comes. Nobody cares. Why doesn't anybody, no matter what I do, why doesn't anybody care about me?

ELS: Wes.

WES: Your life too hard is it?

ELS: Is somebody else hurt, Wes?

WES: Well my life's not great either.

ELS: Wes! Tell me.

WES: No! Nobody else is hurt. Nobody is hurt. Only me.

MUSIC (WHICH CONTINUES THROUGHOUT THE
SCENE). RHYS' HOUSE.
RHYS IS PREPARING, AS SILENTLY AS POSSIBLE, TO GO
TO ELIN'S RESCUE.

RHYS: (QUIETLY) Crap! Crap! Bloody hell Elin! (COMPOSING
HIMSELF) OK. OK.

(HE THINKS HE HEARS HIS MOTHER WAKING.)
Oh crap! Mam! Oh crap, crap!
(HE CONTINUES TO CREEP THROUGH THE HOUSE.)
OK. OK. Keys. Downstairs. Table. (REMEMBERING) Oh! Coat!

(HE PICKS HIS COAT UP. COMING TO HIS SENSES.)
Crap! Mad! Rhys! What are you doing! Go back to bed!
(CHANGING HIS MIND) No! She's waiting for you.
This is your chance! I've got to. Got to!
(HE THINKS HE HEARS HIS SISTER WAKING.) Oh no! Jen!

(HIS MOTHER OBVIOUSLY CALLS OUT TO HIM.
ANSWERING) No! Me.
(BEAT. LISTENING. ANSWERING) Sorry Mam.
(BEAT. LISTENING. ANSWERING) No. I'm fine. Getting a
drink.
(BEAT. ANSWERING) Water! Can't sleep. (BEAT. LISTENING.
ANSWERING) No. I don't think Dad's home yet.
(BEAT. LISTENING. ANSWERING) Yeah. OK.
(BEAT. LISTENING. ANSWERING) Yeah. He must be almost
here. Sorry Mam. Sorry.
(HE LISTENS FOR A MOMENT, BEFORE SPRINGING
BACK INTO ACTION. HE PICKS UP HIS MOTHER'S CAR
KEYS.) Keys!
(HE WALKS SILENTLY THROUGH THE HOUSE.) Hush!
Come on. Come on. Oh crap! Don't believe this.

(HE OPENS THE FRONT DOOR, STEPPING OUT OF THE HOUSE. LOOKING UP HE SEES A LIGHT AT HIS MOTHER'S BEDROOM WINDOW.)

Oh no! Crap Mam! Go back to bed! Please. Please! (BEAT)

(HE GOES TO THE CAR.)

OK. OK. Come on Rhys. Come on.

(HE STRAPS HIMSELF IN.)
Seat belt. Ignition. How hard can it be? Check mirror.
(HE GETS DISTRACTED BY HIS OWN REFLECTION.)
Prick! What am I doing?

(LOOKING UP AT HIS MAM'S BEDROOM WINDOW)
Sorry, Mam. Really really sorry!

(CONCENTRATING ON THE CAR AGAIN) Come on Rhys.
I've seen them do it loads of times.
(HE FIRES THE IGNITION, AND REVS THE ENGINE HARD. SCARED) Oh crap!

(HE TURNS THE IGNITION OFF.)
What was that?! (CALMING DOWN) Come on. Come on!

(HE FIRES THE IGNITION AGAIN, AND REVS THE ENGINE. HAVING SECOND THOUGHTS) No. Whoa. Whoa. What are you doing you prick?! Your Dad could be coming up that road any minute now, and then … (HE IMAGINES TWO CARS CRASHING.)
(SCARED) Oh! Out! Now.

(HE RELEASES HIS SEAT BELT, TO STEP OUT OF THE CAR, BUT CHANGES HIS MIND.)

No! She's waiting for you!
(HE PUTS THE BELT ON AGAIN, BUT CHANGES HIS
MIND.) Out, now!
(HE RELEASES HIS SEAT BELT, BUT CHANGES HIS
MIND.) No I can't. Yes, out. Can't. Can. Can't. I have to!
(CONFUSED. UPSET) Elin! I don't know what to do.

MUSIC.

THE SOUND OF WIND. ON THE CLIFF TOP. BOTH ELIN
AND WES ARE VERY EMOTIONAL. ELIN IS VERY AWARE
OF THE CLIFF EDGE. SHE'S VERY SCARED. WES GRABS
ELIN TO HIM.

WES: A kiss.

ELS: Don't.

WES: One kiss. Come on!

ELS: We're too close to the edge Wes! Don't.

WES: For old time's sake.

ELS: Don't. Please don't.

WES: What?

ELS: I'm scared.

WES: Of what? A kiss?

ELS: No! Falling!

            WES REALISES HOW SCARED ELS IS AND TAKES
            ADVANTAGE OF HER FEAR.

WES: Oh.

ELS: It would hurt. Wouldn't it?

WES: (PULLING HER TOWARDS THE EDGE) Together!

ELS: What?

WES:	You, and me. (SHOUTS) Flying!
ELS:	No!
WES:	(SHOUTING) Free!
ELS:	No!
WES:	Why? Beautiful and soft up there you said. (BEAT) Or if you don't want to fly, dive then, into the warm sea! (BEAT) We'd have to count though!
ELS:	What?
WES:	One, two, three! In case one of us misleads the other.
	ELIN CRIES.
	Everybody would be talking about us. We'd be on the news! (AS A JOURNALIST) 'Today two bodies were swept ashore by crashing waves. No ordinary bodies. A merman and mermaid.'
ELS:	No!
WES:	Seconds! That's all it would take. Before we landed.
ELS:	Landing sounds good.
WES:	Yeah?
ELS:	It wouldn't be though Wes! We'd be on those rocks down there. Broken!
WES:	It'd be in the papers. (BEAT) I wonder if Mam and Dad would see it?
ELS:	Wes!
WES:	Wonder if they'd care?

ELS: Of course they would.

WES: Yeah? I'm talking about my parents, Elin. Not yours.

ELS: Our bones would break.

WES: My parents have never been there for me.

ELS: There'd be blood. A lot of blood. It would hurt.

WES: What?

ELS: Wouldn't it? Wouldn't it?

WES: Hurt you? How should I know?

ELS: What?

WES: How am I supposed to know what hurts you? I don't understand your pain do I?

ELS: What?

WES: Posh pain! The only sort of pain I understand is getting a kicking isn't it?

ELS: Sorry.

WES: But you don't understand that sort of pain either do you? Do you? (BEAT) Why did you let me think your dad hit you?

ELS: It just happened.

WES: Did it?

ELS: Yeah.

WES: Did it?

ELS: Yes! I think! I don't know! I'm sorry!

WES: Are you? (WES IS PULLING HER TOWARDS THE EDGE) Come on.

ELS: What? No! (BEAT) What if someone down there sees us?

WES: What?

ELS: Someone. Down there!

WES: Who?

ELS: I don't know! Someone! I'm not sure!

WES: What are they going to do? Give us a bollocking?

ELS: Don't.

WES: While we're falling is it? (AS ON-LOOKER) 'What do you think you're doing up there? Bloody ruffians!' Or after we land? (AS ON-LOOKER) 'Look at the mess you've made! Young kids these days!' (PULLING HER CLOSER TO THE EDGE) Or maybe they'll try to catch us!

ELS: No Wes! No! No!

WES: There's nobody there. Look. No-one at all. Only us!

ELS: No. No-one. I know I'm not thinking straight.

WES: No?

ELS: No.

WES: You don't want to, do you? (BEAT) Life's not as bad as you thought is it?

ELS: I don't know.

WES: (WITH CONTEMPT) Don't know? You don't know?

ELS: I'm not sure.

WES: (COMMANDING) A kiss.
         (HE TRIES TO KISS HER. SHE RESISTS.)
         A kiss. Here. Now. And then decide.

         THEY KISS. THE WIND BLOWS LOUDER FOR A
         MOMENT, DYING DOWN AS WES AND ELIN SEPARATE.

         PAUSE.

         Well? Are we going? Are we? Are we?

         ELIN SHAKES HER HEAD.

         Good choice Elin. (BEAT) Nobody's ever cared about me right, but
         I'm going to be OK. Know why? 'Cause I've decided. Me. So if my
         life's worth having Elin, I know your life is definitely worth living.

ELS: Sorry Wes. (BEAT) I'm really sorry! Where are you going?

WES: Cop shop.

ELIN: Sorry.

WES: Someone's car's smashed up outside town.

ELIN: I'll come with you.

WES: Get lost.

ELIN: You need the hospital.

WES: Get lost Elin. I don't need you.

         WES EXITS.

LONG PAUSE.

ELIN REMEMBERS RHYS. SHE PHONES HIM, BUT
THERE IS NO ANSWER.

Oh!

SHE PHONES HIM AGAIN, BUT THERE IS NO REPLY.

ELS: Pick up Rhys. Pick up. Pick up!

RESPONDING TO ANSWER PHONE, SHE LEAVES A
MESSAGE.

Hope you get this Rhys. Sorry, OK? I don't need you to come now.
OK? Going home. I'm OK. I'm fine. (TO HERSELF) Please Rhys,
don't do anything silly. You wouldn't though would you? Never. Too
clever. (BEAT) Talk tomorrow. Yeah. (BEAT) Talk to everyone,
tomorrow.

ELIN LEAVES.

MUSIC.